How to Dazzle at

BEING

SCIENTIST

Jean Stanbury

Brilliant Publications

We hope you and your class enjoy using this book. Other books in the series include:

How to Dazzle at Writing	1 897675 45 3
How to Dazzle at Reading	1 897675 44 5
How to Dazzle at Spelling	1 897675 47 X
How to Dazzle at Grammar	1 897675 46 1

Other science books available include:

How to be Brilliant at Science Investigations	1 897675 11 9
How to be Brilliant at Recording in Science	1 897675 10 0
How to be Brilliant at Materials	1 897675 12 7
How to be Brilliant at Electricity, Light and Sound	1 897675 13 5

If you would like further information on these or other titles published by Brilliant Publications, please write to the address given below.

Published by Brilliant Publications, The Old School Yard, Leighton Road, Northall, Dunstable, Bedfordshire LU6 2HA

Written by Jean Stanbury
Illustrated by Michelle Ives

Printed in Malta by Interprint Ltd

© Jean Stanbury 1999
ISBN 1 897675 52 6

First published 1999
10 9 8 7 6 5 4 3 2 1

Contents

Introduction

The worksheets are aimed at pupils working at Key Stage 3 (11 – 14 year olds).

The procedures are given in clear, step-by-step instructions. Illustrations are found alongside the text to enable the pupil to have a clear understanding of what is required.

The worksheets are intended both for pupils with special educational needs and for pupils who are more able. The worksheets enable the pupil with special educational needs to home in on the key words and concepts in a very practical way and to record his/her findings without the daunting task of too much written work. Teachers should feel free to adapt the sheets (eg by deleting certain sections) to make them suitable for their pupils.

Importantly the worksheets are differentiated for the more able pupils, enabling them to question further by completing the 'Add-on' activities at the bottom of the sheets. The worksheets could also be used as a base for sequencing procedures, providing appropriate headings for the pupils when they are writing up their experiments in full.

On page 20 we recommend the use of a mercury thermometer. If your authority does not permit the use of mercury thermometers in schools, then you can substitute a spirit or alcohol thermometer, but you will be unable to measure the temperature of boiling water.

Links to the National Curriculum at Key Stage 3

How to Dazzle at Being a Scientist relates directly to the requirements for:

- safe procedure
- obtaining evidence
- analysing evidence and drawing conclusions
- evaluating the evidence and recognizing anomalies.

Processes and Living Things
Microscope work – animals and plants are made up of cells – 1b
Nutrition – food tests – 2
Green plants as organisms – testing for the presence of starch in a leaf – 3a

Materials and their properties
Classifying materials – gas pressure and diffusion – 1c
Separating techniques – includes filtration, distillation and chromatography – 1i
Patterns of behaviour – reactions of metals with acids – 3a
Finding the pH of a solution – 3f
Using indicators to classify solutions – 3f
Reactions of acids with metals, bases and carbonates – 3g
Neutralization – 3h

Physical processes
Electricity and magnetism – how to measure a current in series and parallel circuits – 1c
Materials which are attracted to a magnet – 1g
The field pattern produced by a magnet – 1h
Electromagnets – 1j
Light and sound – how light is reflected at plane surfaces – 3e
How light is refracted through glass – 3f
White light can be dispersed to give a range of colours – 3g

Other areas covered include basic laboratory skills such as using a Bunsen burner, measuring cylinder, digital balance and thermometer, and preparing salts.

How to plan an investigation

Answer the questions using complete sentences.

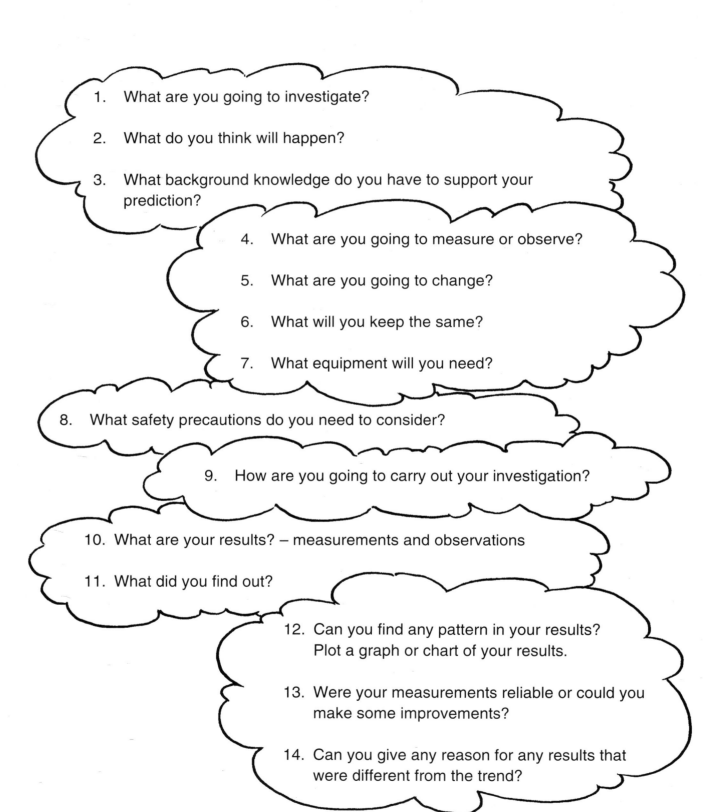

1. What are you going to investigate?

2. What do you think will happen?

3. What background knowledge do you have to support your prediction?

4. What are you going to measure or observe?

5. What are you going to change?

6. What will you keep the same?

7. What equipment will you need?

8. What safety precautions do you need to consider?

9. How are you going to carry out your investigation?

10. What are your results? – measurements and observations

11. What did you find out?

12. Can you find any pattern in your results? Plot a graph or chart of your results.

13. Were your measurements reliable or could you make some improvements?

14. Can you give any reason for any results that were different from the trend?

How to use a Bunsen burner

Safety
- Tie long hair back.
- Always wear safety goggles.
- Never leave a Bunsen burner unattended.

Label the parts of the Bunsen burner using these words:

air hole
base
jet
chimney
collar

To gas tap

Procedure

Place the Bunsen burner is a safe position – not near the edge of the bench.
Place the Bunsen burner on a ceramic mat.
Make sure the air hole is closed. Then light the burner.

Different flames

What colour is the flame when the air hole is closed? _____

What do we call this type of flame? _____

What colour is the flame when the air hole is fully open? _____

What do we call this type of flame? _____

Hold a piece of pottery using a pair of tongs in a blue flame. Then hold it in a yellow flame. What differences do you see? Can you explain why?

_____

_____

How to heat substances

What you need
- 3 test tubes
- Bunsen burner
- Test tube holder
- Ceramic mat
- Spatulas
- Zinc oxide
- Copper carbonate
- Copper sulphate
- Goggles

Safety
- Always tie long hair back.
- Always wear safety goggles.
- Angle the test tube away from you when heating.
- Never look down the test tube.
- Use a small amount of chemical.

Procedure

Use a clean spatula. Place a small amount of zinc oxide into one of the clean test tubes. Place the test tube in the test tube rack. Do the same for the other two chemicals. Use a clean spatula each time.

Place the Bunsen burner on a ceramic mat. Make sure it is in a safe position on the bench.

Light the Bunsen burner with the air hole closed.

Hold the test tube with zinc oxide in a blue flame using a test tube holder until a colour change occurs.

Return the test tube to the rack. Record changes in colour that take place during heating and cooling in the table. Then heat the other two test tubes.

Name of chemical	Colour before heating	Colour during heating	Colour when cooled

Wait until the test tube containing the copper sulphate has cooled. Then add a few drops of water. What happens?

_____

Why do you think this happens?

_____

_____

Add-on
What compound is formed when copper carbonate is heated?

Evaporation

Safety
- Always tie long hair back.
- Always wear safety goggles.
- Take care when stirring hot liquids.

Procedure

Place four spatulas of sodium chloride (salt) into a 250 ml beaker. Add 50 ml of water. Stir with a glass rod to dissolve the salt.

Salt + water

Place the Bunsen burner on a ceramic mat. Make sure it is in a safe position on the bench. Place a tripod over the Bunsen burner. Put the pipe clay triangle on top.

Carefully pour the salt solution into the evaporating basin so that it is half full. Place the basin on top of the pipe clay triangle.

Light the Bunsen burner with the air hole closed. Heat the solution with a small blue flame.

Stir the contents with a glass rod. When crystals start forming on the end of the glass rod, turn off the gas. Let it sit to allow the crystals to form.

Evaporating basin with salt solution

When the evaporating basin has cooled, use a hand lens to look at the salt crystals. Draw what you see in the box below.

Add-on

Repeat the procedure using copper sulphate and zinc sulphate.
Draw the crystals that are formed. Are all the crystals the same shape?

Shape of sodium chloride crystals	Shape of copper sulphate crystals	Shape of zinc sulphate crystals

How to Dazzle at Being a Scientist

How to use a microscope

What you need
- Microscope
- Prepared microscope slide of an onion cell

Safety
- Always support the microscope underneath when handling it.
- Place the microscope on a flat surface.

What you should know

A **microscope** enables us to see things that are too small to be seen with the naked eye.

A famous scientist by the name of Robert Hooke put forward the idea that living things are built up of building blocks which he called **cells**. A microscope is used to magnify these cells.

Label the parts of the microscope using the following words:

adjustment knob
mirror
objective lens
eyepiece
stage

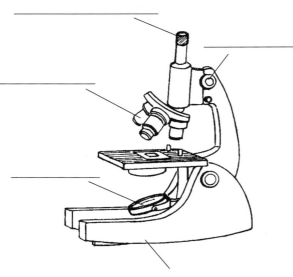

Procedure

Hold the prepared slide on the edge to avoid getting finger marks on it. Place the slide on the stage of the microscope. Rotate the low power objective lens into position. Adjust the mirror so that light is reflected into the microscope.

Looking at the side of the microscope, carefully turn the adjustment knob so that the objective lens and the stage are close to each other.

Look down the eyepiece. Turn the adjustment knob slowly to bring the onion cell into focus. This is called **focusing**.

Repeat the focusing procedure using a higher power objective lens.

Draw what you see on a separate sheet of paper. Label the cell.

Add-on
If the eyepiece has a magnification of x10 and the objective lens has a magnification of x4, what is the total magnification?

How to prepare a microscope slide

Safety
- Take care when handling sharp instruments.
- Iodine is harmful.
- Always support the microscope underneath when handling it.
- Place the microscope on a flat surface.

Procedure
Place the onion on the white tile and cut a small section using a scalpel.

Hold the section of onion in place using a seeker. Remove the transparent skin from the fleshy part of the onion using a pair of forceps.

Place the transparent skin on the slide, making sure it lies flat. Remember to hold the glass slide on the edge to avoid finger marks.

Place a drop of iodine on the transparent skin. Place the cover slip on top, lowering it into position using the seeker. Absorb any excess iodine with the filter paper.

Why do you think iodine is used?

_____

Use the microscope to look at the onion cells.
Draw what you see, in the box below.

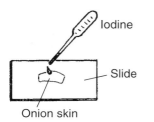

Section of onion — Transparent skin — White tile

Iodine — Slide — Onion skin

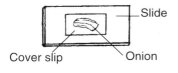

Slide — Cover slip — Onion

Add-on
Make slides using elodea and tomato.

Onion	Elodea	Tomato

How to separate the substances found in rock salt

What you need
- Rock salt
- Spatula
- Pestle and mortar
- 250 cm³ beaker
- 25 cm³ measuring cylinder
- Glass rod
- 250 cm³ conical flask
- Filter funnel
- Filter paper
- Evaporating basin
- Pipe clay triangle
- Tripod
- Bunsen burner
- Ceramic mat
- Goggles

Safety
- Tie long hair back.
- Always wear safety goggles.
- Never leave the Bunsen burner unattended.

Procedure

1. Measure out four spatulas of rock salt. Grind them into smaller lumps using a pestle and mortar. Put three spatulas of the rock salt into a 250 cm³ beaker. Add 25 cm³ of water. Stir using a glass rod.

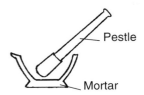

Pestle

Mortar

2. Put the funnel into a 250 cm³ conical flask and put the filter paper in the funnel. Put a glass rod in the filter paper.

Pour the rock salt mixture carefully into the filter paper. Allow the mixture to run down the glass rod into the centre of the funnel. Do not overfill the funnel.

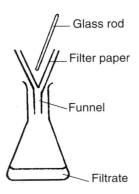

Glass rod

Filter paper

Funnel

Filtrate

3. What is left behind in the filter paper? This is called the **residue**.

_____

What has happened to the salt?

_____

4. Transfer the liquid in the bottom of the conical flask to an evaporating basin. This liquid is called the **filtrate**. Place the basin on a pipe clay triangle on a tripod. Heat it gently over a Bunsen burner. Stir with a glass rod. Wait until crystals start forming on the end of the glass rod. Remove the basin from the heat. Allow it to cool.

Rock salt in evaporating basin

What is left behind in the evaporating basin?

_____

Add-on
What other substances could be separated by filtering?

How to separate coloured dyes

What you need
- Coloured food dyes
- Glass rod
- Chromatography paper
- Wooden splint
- Paper clip
- 250 cm³ beaker
- Pencil
- Ruler
For Add-on
- Felt-tipped pens

What you should know
Chromatography is a way of separating coloured dyes by dissolving them in water.

When **chromatography pape**r is partly immersed in water, any dyes on the paper separate as the water is absorbed by the paper.

Procedure
You are going to make a **chromatogram**. Cut a 10 cm long strip of chromatography paper. Draw a pencil line on the strip of chromatography paper 2 cm from the bottom edge. Draw a cross in the centre of the line.

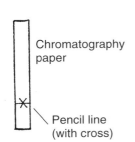

Chromatography paper

Pencil line (with cross)

Dip the end of the glass rod into one of the food dyes. Transfer a small blob of food dye on to the cross.

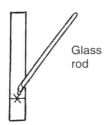

Glass rod

Fill a 250 cm³ beaker with water to a depth of 1.5 cm. Attach the top of the chromatography paper to a wooden splint using a paper clip. Place the end of the chromatography paper into the water. Make sure that the dye stays above the water level.

Why do you think it is important for the dye to be above the water level?

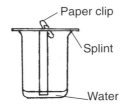

Paper clip

Splint

Water

_____

Leave the chromatogram to run.

Fill in the missing words:
As the water rises up the paper, it d __ __ __ __ __ __ __ __ coloured chemicals and

c __ __ __ __ __ __ them up the paper.

When the dye has finished separating, take the paper out of the water. Leave it to dry. What colours was the dye made up of?

_____

Attach your chromatogram to the back of this worksheet.

Add-on
Repeat using other coloured dyes or felt-tipped pens.

How to separate salt from salt water by distillation

What you need
- Salt
- Spatula
- 100 cm³ beaker
- 25 cm³ measuring cylinder
- Water
- Glass rod
- Boiling tube fitted with delivery tube and bung
- Test tube
- Beaker
- Bunsen burner
- Ceramic mat
- Goggles

Safety
- Tie long hair back.
- Always wear safety goggles.
- Never leave the Bunsen burner unattended.

Procedure
Put three spatulas of salt into a 100 cm³ beaker.
Add 20 cm³ of water. Stir with a glass rod to dissolve the salt.

Pour the salt solution into a boiling tube to a depth of 3 cm.

Attach the bung on the delivery tube to the mouth of the boiling tube.

Place a test tube under the end of the delivery tube and place the test tube in a beaker of water.

Heat the salt solution gently.

What do you see rising up the delivery tube?

_____

Fill in the missing words:
What happened when the water vapour came in contact with the cold test tube?

It c __ __ __ __ __ __ __ __ .

What collected in the test tube?

_____

What remained in the boiling tube?

_____

Distillation can be used to separate a

s __ __ __ __ from a s __ __ __ __ __ .

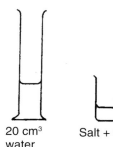

20 cm³ water   Salt + water

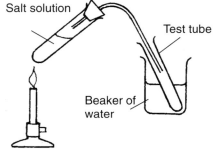

Salt solution   Test tube

Beaker of water

Add-on
Fractional distillation is used to separate liquids with different

b __ __ __ __ __ __ __ p __ __ __ __ __ .

How to separate paraffin from water

What you need
- Separating funnel
- Clamp stand
- 250 cm³ beaker
- Coloured paraffin
- Water
- Beaker
- Goggles

Safety
- Always wear safety goggles.
- Paraffin is flammable.

What you should know

When two liquids do not mix they can be separated using a separating funnel.

Liquids that will not dissolve into each other are called **immiscible**.

Liquids that separate out into two layers are called **emulsions**. Some liquid medicines and a type of paint are emulsions.

Procedure

Close the tap on the separating funnel.

Add water until it is about a third full. Pour in the coloured paraffin to a depth of 3 cm.

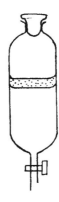

Place the stopper in position. Gently shake the separating funnel. To do this place the stopper end against the palm of your hand. Every few shakes, turn the flask so that the tap is pointing upwards and release the pressure by opening the tap with your other hand.

Allow the mixture to separate. Leave it to stand until the liquids form two separate layers.

What do we call a mixture which will separate out into two liquids when it is left to stand?

An e __ __ __ __ __ __ .

Remove the stopper. Open the tap and run the bottom layer of liquid into a beaker. Take care towards the end of the separation. Turn the tap so that the liquid drips through.

What liquid is left behind in the separating funnel?

_____

Add-on
What other liquids could be separated using this method?

How to use a measuring cylinder

What you need
- 10 cm³ measuring cylinder
- 25 cm³ measuring cylinder
- 100 cm³ measuring cylinder
- Goggles
  For Add-on
- Small pebble

Safety
- Tie long hair back.
- Always wear safety goggles.
- Stand the measuring cylinders on a flat surface.

What you should know

Liquids form a curved surface inside the measuring cylinder.
This is called a **meniscus**.

In a 100 cm³ measuring cylinder, each division represents _____ cm³.

In a 10 cm³ measuring cylinder, each division represents _____ cm³.

In a 25 cm³ measuring cylinder, each division represents _____ cm³.

Procedure

Half fill the 10 cm³ measuring cylinder with water. Place the measuring cylinder on a level surface. Keeping your eye level with the bottom of the water level, record the volume of water.

Volume of water in 10 cm³ cylinder = _____ cm³.

Repeat the procedure using the 25 cm³ and 100 cm³ measuring cylinders.

Volume of water in 25 cm³ cylinder = _____ cm³.

Volume of water in 100 cm³ cylinder = _____ cm³.

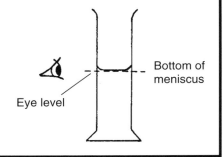

Eye level

Bottom of meniscus

Add-on

Use your skill to find the volume of a pebble.
Half fill the 100 cm³ measuring cylinder with water.
Record the volume of water: _____ cm³.
Carefully drop a small pebble into the measuring cylinder.
Record the volume: _____ cm³.

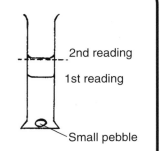

2nd reading

1st reading

Small pebble

To find the volume of the pebble:

> volume of water + pebble − volume of water at start = volume of pebble

How to use a metre rule

What you need
- Metre rule
- Pencil

What you should know
A metre rule is 100 centimetres long. This can be written as 100 cm.

Finish these sentences.
There are 10 millimetres in 1 centimetre. This can be written as 10 mm.

There are 100 centimetres in 1 _____ .

There are 1000 metres in 1 _____ .

Look at these metre rules.

The reading on this metre rule would be 0.5 cm or 5 mm.

What is the reading on this metre rule?

_____ cm.

What is the reading on this metre rule?

_____ cm.

Procedure
Work in pairs.

Use the metre rule to fill in the chart.

The length of the workbench			cm
The height of the workbench			cm
Your partner's height		m	cm
Your height		m	cm

How to use a digital balance

What you need
- Digital balance
- Beaker
- Conical flask
- Test tube
- Test tube holder
- Tongs
- Evaporating basin
- Spatula
- Watch glass
- Salt
- Balance brush

Safety
- Always place the digital balance on an uncluttered, level workbench.
- Do not lean on the workbench when using the balance as this may affect the reading.
- Always keep the pan clean and never drop things on to the pan.
- Never weigh hot things on the balance.

Label the diagram using these words:
pan
weight in grams
tare (T) button

A balance is used to measure mass in units called _____ .

Procedure
1. Zero the balance by pressing the T button (or tare button) when the pan is empty. The balance is now ready to use.
2. To find the mass of an object, place the object on the pan. Read and record the mass.
3. Zero the balance by pressing the T button before placing the next object on the pan.
4. Weigh several objects. Record the mass of each object in the table below.

To weigh one gram of salt, place the watch glass on the pan. Press the T button. The balanced will now be zeroed. Carefully add the salt to the watch glass using a spatula until the reading in the display is 1.0 g. If salt spills on to the pan, switch off the balance, dust off the salt using a balance brush, and start again.

Name of object	Mass in gram(s)

How to demonstrate Hooke's law

Safety
- Handle slotted weights carefully to avoid dropping them on your toes.
- Take care not to overstretch the spring. When the force is removed the spring must return to its original length.

Procedure

Clamp a metre rule in position, as shown in the diagram.

Attach the spring to the claw of the clamp so that the spring lies against the metre rule.

Attach the hanger under the spring. Tape a paper clip under the hanger.

Use the paper clip as a point for the metre rule readings. Record the reading on the metre rule with no weights on the hanger. Write it in the table below.

Add the 20 g slotted weights to the hanger, one at a time. Record the reading on the metre rule after each addition.

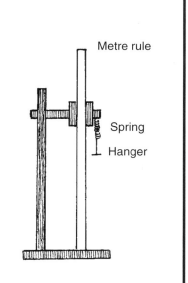

Metre rule

Spring

Hanger

Weight in grams	Reading in cm
0	
20	
40	
60	
80	
100	
120	
140	

Plot a graph of load versus extension.

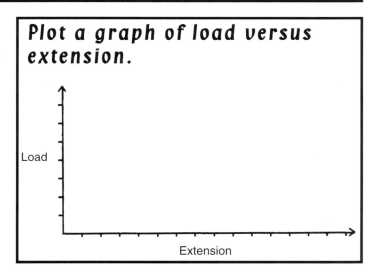

Load

Extension

What do you notice about the shape of the graph? _____

Can you make up a rule for your findings? _____

_____

How to use a thermometer

What you need
- Thermometer
- 250 cm^3 beaker
- Crushed ice
- Water
- Bunsen burner
- Tripod
- Gauze
- Ceramic mat
- Goggles

Safety
- Handle the thermometer with care as it is made of glass.
- Always place the thermometer in a safe position, so that it does not roll off the bench.
- Wear safety goggles when heating the water.

Label the diagram using these words:
bulb
thin glass
thick glass
mercury
scale

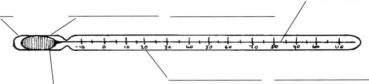

Thermometers tell us how hot or cold something is. They measure temperature in degrees Celsius (ºC). The bulb of the thermometer is made of thin glass so that it can detect rapidly any change in the temperature. It contains a silver liquid called **mercury**. The stem is made of thick glass. It has an inner fine capillary tube running along its length. The mercury expands up and contracts down this fine tube as the temperature of the mercury in the bulb changes.

The scale on the side of the thermometer goes from _____ºC to _____ ºC.

How to find the temperature of the room
Hold the thermometer by the stem. When the level of the mercury is steady, record the temperature.

Temperature of room _____ ºC

How to find the temperature of crushed ice
Place some crushed ice in a beaker. Surround the bulb of the thermometer with the ice. Leave the thermometer in the beaker. When the mercury is steady, take the reading of the thermometer.

Temperature of ice _____ ºC

How to find the temperature of boiling water
Half fill a 250 cm^3 beaker with water. Heat the water using a Bunsen burner. When the water is boiling, turn off the Bunsen burner. Place the thermometer in the water. Record the temperature when the mercury is steady.

Temperature of boiling water _____ ºC

How to detect acids and alkalis

Safety
- Both acids and alkalis carry hazard signs and must be handled with care.
- What hazard signs are on the bottles?

Acid _____   Alkali _____

What you should know
Indicators are chemicals which change colour when they are added to an acid or an alkali. One common indicator is **litmus**. Litmus turns red in an acidic solution and blue in an alkaline one.

Procedure

1. Label three test tubes as **hydrochloric acid**. Using a test pipette, add 2 cm depth of hydrochloric acid to each test tube.

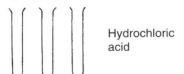

Hydrochloric acid

2. Label three other test tubes as **sodium hydroxide**. Using a teat pipette, add 2 cm depth of sodium hydroxide to each of the test tubes.

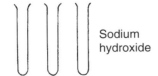

Sodium hydroxide

3. Add a few drops of litmus to one of the test tubes containing hydrochloric acid. Add a few drops of litmus to one of the test tubes containing sodium hydroxide.

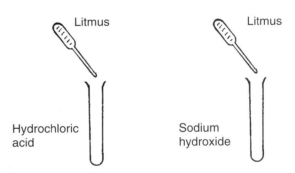

Litmus   Litmus

Hydrochloric acid   Sodium hydroxide

Repeat Step 3 using phenolphthalein and methyl orange indicators. Record how the colour changes in the table.

	Indicator	Starting colour	Final colour
Hydrochloric acid	Litmus		
Sodium hydroxide	Litmus		
Hydrochloric acid	Phenolphthalein		
Sodium hydroxide	Phenolphthalein		
Hydrochloric acid	Methyl orange		
Sodium hydroxide	Methyl orange		

How to Dazzle at Being a Scientist

How do carbonates react with acids?

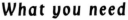

What you need
- 6 test tubes
- Test tube rack
- Teat pipette
- Spatula
- Calcium carbonate
- Sodium bicarbonate
- Copper carbonate
- Dilute hydrochloric acid
- Limewater
- Delivery tube fitted with bung
- Goggles

Safety
- Wear safety goggles.
- Tie long hair back.
- Acids are corrosive and should be handled with care.

Procedure

1. Add a spatula of calcium carbonate to a test tube.

2. Using a teat pipette, add about 1 cm depth of dilute hydrochloric acid to the carbonate in the test tube.

3. Connect the bung on the delivery tube to the mouth of the test tube.

4. Place the other end of the delivery tube into a test tube of limewater.

5. Put the test tubes in a test tube rack. Leave them there until the reaction is completed.

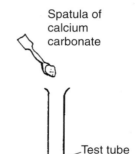

Spatula of calcium carbonate

Test tube

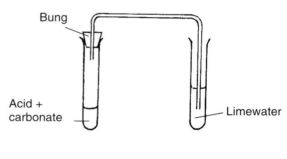

Bung

Acid + carbonate

Limewater

Repeat steps 1 – 5 for sodium bicarbonate and copper carbonate.

What does this tell us about the reaction of acids on carbonates?

_____

What are the products of the reaction?

carbonate   +   _____   +   _____

Why does the limewater go cloudy?

_____

What is formed?

_____

How do metals react with acids?

What you need
- 8 test tubes
- Test tube rack
- Spatula
- Zinc
- Iron filings
- Copper
- Magnesium ribbon
- Ethanoic acid
- Hydrochloric acid
- Bunsen burner
- Ceramic mats
- Splints
- Labels for test tubes
- Goggles

Safety
- Wear safety goggles.
- Tie long hair back.
- Acids are corrosive and should be handled with care.

Procedure

1. Label four test tubes as **ethanoic acid**. Pour 1 cm depth of acid into each of the test tubes. Place them in a test tube rack.

Ethanoic acid

2. Label four test tubes as **hydrochloric acid**. Pour 1 cm depth of acid into each of the test tubes. Place them in a test tube rack.

Hydrochloric acid

3. Add a spatula of zinc to one of the test tubes containing ethanoic acid and to one containing hydrochloric acid.

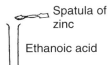
Spatula of zinc
Ethanoic acid
Spatula of zinc
Hydrochloric acid

4. Hold a lighted splint to the mouth of the test tube to test for the presence of hydrogen.

Lighted splint
Acid + metal

Repeat steps 3 and 4 for the iron filings, copper, and magnesium. Record your results in the table. Which acid produces a quicker reaction?

Metal	Is hydrogen produced with ethanoic acid?	Is hydrogen produced with hydrochloric acid?

Add-on
Complete the word equation for each metal that reacts with the hydrochloric acid.

metal + hydrochloric acid ⟶ _____ + _____

How to find the pH of a solution

What you need
- A selection of household products: toothpaste, shampoo, fizzy drink, vinegar, cream cleaner, bleach, citric acid, sodium chloride solution
- Universal indicator paper
- Colour chart
- White tile
- Glass rod
- Paper towel
- Goggles

Safety
- Wear safety goggles when handling chemicals.
- See how many of the products carry a hazard sign.
- Wipe up any spillages.

What you should know

Universal indicator can detect whether a solution is an **acid** or an **alkali**. It also measures how strong the acid or alkali is on a scale from 1 to 14. This is called the **pH scale**. For example, hydrochloric acid is a strong acid whereas vinegar is a weak acid. Each pH value has a corresponding indicator colour.

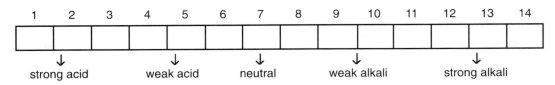

1	2	3	4	5	6	7	8	9	10	11	12	13	14

strong acid   weak acid   neutral   weak alkali   strong alkali

Procedure

Put a piece of universal indicator paper on to a white tile. Place the end of a clean glass rod into one of the household products. Transfer some of the household product on to the universal indicator paper. Record the colour change.

Wash the end of the glass rod. Repeat the procedure with other household products. Use a fresh piece of paper each time.

Use the colour chart to match up the colour with that produced by each solution. Record the pH value in the chart.

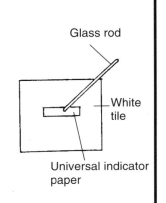

Glass rod

White tile

Universal indicator paper

Household product	Colour of indicator paper	pH	Acid or alkali?

How to make a neutral solution

What you need
- 25 cm^3 measuring cylinder
- 100 cm^3 beaker
- Glass rod
- Spatula
- Bunsen burner
- Ceramic mat
- Teat pipette
- 1M hydrochloric acid
- 1M sodium hydroxide
- Universal indicator paper
- Colour chart
- White tile
- Glass rod
- Goggles

Safety
- Always wear safety goggles.
- Tie long hair back.
- Acids and bases are corrosive and should be handled with care.

What you should know
Acids and alkalis are chemical opposites.
An acid will react with an alkali.
This process is called **neutralization**.

Procedure

1. Measure out 20 cm^3 of hydrochloric acid. Pour the acid into a 100 cm^3 beaker.

   20 cm^3 hydrochloric acid

   Beaker

2. Place a strip of universal indicator paper on a white tile. Dip the end of the glass rod into the hydrochloric acid and place it on to the strip of universal indicator paper.

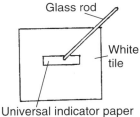

   Glass rod

   White tile

   Universal indicator paper

   What colour does the indicator paper turn?

   _____

3. Add a drop of sodium hydroxide to the acid in the beaker. Use the teat pipette. Stir using a glass rod.

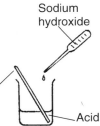

   Sodium hydroxide

   Glass rod

   Acid

   Keep adding more sodium hydroxide, a drop at a time. Stir the contents after each addition. Use the glass rod and fresh indicator paper to note the colour changes. Match these colour changes with the colour chart.

   How will you know when the solution is neutral?

   _____

   When the neutralization point has been reached, stop adding the sodium hydroxide.

   What should you do if the indicator paper turns blue?

   _____

Add-on
Find out how to neutralize wasp stings and bee stings.

How to make sodium chloride

Safety
- Always wear safety goggles.
- Tie long hair back.
- Handle all acids and alkalis with care.

Procedure

1. Measure out 20 cm³ of hydrochloric acid. Pour it into a 100 cm³ beaker.

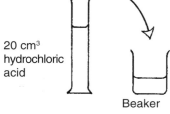

20 cm³ hydrochloric acid

Beaker

2. Carefully dip the end of the glass rod into the acid. Place the end on to the universal indicator paper, on the white tile.

   What colour does the acid turn the universal indicator paper?

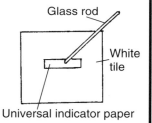

Glass rod

White tile

Universal indicator paper

___ ___ ___

3. Add a drop of 1M sodium hydroxide to the acid in the beaker using a teat pipette. Stir the contents using a glass rod.

   Place a drop on to a fresh piece of universal indicator paper using the glass rod. Record any colour change.

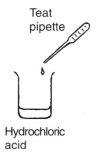

Teat pipette

Hydrochloric acid

4. Continue adding sodium hydroxide. Do this a drop at a time, until the neutralization point is reached.

   What colour does the indicator go in a neutral solution?

   ___ ___ ___ ___ ___

5. Transfer the neutral solution to an evaporating basin. Heat the solution gently using a Bunsen burner. Stir the contents using a glass rod. When crystals start forming on the end of the glass rod, leave the evaporating basin to cool.

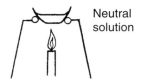

Neutral solution

   What is the name of the salt you have made?

   _____

Add-on
Use a hand lens to look at the crystals. Draw what you see.

How to make copper sulphate

Safety
- Wear safety goggles.
- Tie long hair back.
- Handle all acids with care.

Procedure

1. Measure out 25 cm³ of dilute sulphuric acid into a small beaker.

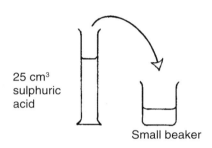

25 cm³ sulphuric acid

Small beaker

Heat gently using a Bunsen burner. Do not let the acid boil.

2. Add one spatula of copper oxide powder to the acid. Stir with a glass rod. Keep adding it, one spatula at a time, until no more will dissolve.

 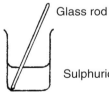

Glass rod

Sulphuric acid

Copper oxide

3. Wait until the contents of the beaker are cool enough to handle. Then filter the contents.

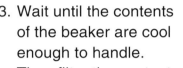

Copper oxide

Salt solution

4. Pour the filtrate into an evaporating basin. Heat gently. Stir continuously with a glass rod until one half the original volume remains.

Leave the salt solution to cool. On a separate sheet of paper, draw the crystals. Use a hand lens to help you.

Salt solution

Complete the equations.

| sulphuric acid | + | copper oxide | $\longrightarrow$ | _ _ _ _ _ _ _ _ _ _ _ _ _ _ | + | water |

| acid | + | base | $\longrightarrow$ | _ _ _ _ _ | + | _ _ _ _ _ _ |

How to make zinc sulphate

Safety
- Tie long hair back.
- Always wear safety goggles.
- Handle all acids with care.

Procedure

1. Measure out 25 cm^3 of dilute sulphuric acid into a small beaker. Add three drops of copper sulphate solution. Add three pieces of zinc. Warm the contents gently using a Bunsen burner.

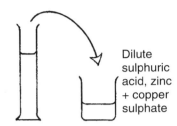

Dilute sulphuric acid, zinc + copper sulphate

2. Wait until the zinc has finished reacting. Let it cool. Then filter the contents. Transfer the filtrate to an evaporating dish.

   What gas was given off when the acid reacted with the zinc? _____

Small pieces of zinc

Filtrate

3. Heat the salt solution gently. Stir continuously with a glass rod. Keep heating the filtrate until half the original volume has evaporated.

Salt solution

4. Leave the evaporating basin to cool so that the crystals can form. Draw the crystals on a separate sheet of paper. Use a hand lens to help you.

Crystals left to grow

Fill in the missing words.

The copper sulphate acted as a c __ __ __ __ __ __ __ __ and
s __ __ __ __ __ __ up the reaction.

Complete the equation.

zinc   +   sulphuric acid $\longrightarrow$ z __ __ __   +   h __ __ __ __ __ __ __ __
                                                s __ __ __ __ __ __ __

What happens when light hits a mirror?

What you need
- Ray box
- Low voltage power supply
- Card with narrow slit
- Mirror
- Bulldog clip
- White paper
- Pencil
- Ruler
- Protractor

Procedure

Draw a pencil line on the white paper. Place the back surface of the mirror along the line.

Attach the bulldog clip to the mirror to stop it falling over.

Fit the slit card on to the ray box. Direct the ray of light towards the mirror. Draw two crosses on the paper to show where the ray of light goes before it hits the mirror. Draw two more crosses on the ray of light reflected by the mirror.

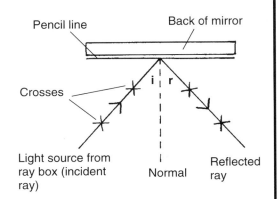

Switch off the light source. Join up the crosses. Use your protractor to construct a line at 90º to the mirror, as shown by the dotted line in the diagram. This line is called the **normal**. The angles of the rays striking and leaving the mirror are usually measured from the normal.

Measure the angles marked **i** and **r** in the diagram using a protractor.

Move the ray box. Repeat the experiment so that the light strikes the mirror from a different position.

What is the ray going towards the mirror called?

_____ ray

What is the ray coming away from the mirror called?

_____ ray

What do you notice about the size of the angles for the incident and the reflected rays?

_____

What happens when light travels through glass?

What you need
- Glass block
- White paper
- Ray box
- Card with narrow slit
- Pencil
- Ruler
- Protractor

Procedure

Place a glass block on a piece of white paper. Draw round the block using a pencil.

Fit the slit card on the ray box. Switch on the light source. Direct the beam of light so that it passes through the glass block. Mark two crosses on the light path entering the glass block. Mark two crosses on the light path leaving the glass block.

Switch off the light source and remove the glass block. Join up the crosses using a pencil and ruler. Finally, draw a line across where the glass block was, so that you join the rays entering and leaving the glass block. Use the protractor to construct 90º angles as shown by the lines marked **N** and **n** on the diagram. Measure the angles **i** and **r**.

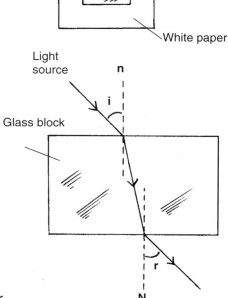

When light passes from one material into another, it changes direction. This is called **refraction**.

What is the beam of light going into the block called?

_____ ray

What is the beam of light coming out of the block called?

_____ ray

Can you explain why a stick appears bent in water?

_____

_____

_____

Add-on
Light travels at different speeds through different materials. Find out how fast light travels in air.

How to find which colours make up white light

What you need
- Ray box
- Low voltage power supply
- Card with narrow slit
- Prism
- White screen

What you should know

White light is made up of the seven colours that are found in a rainbow. When it rains each raindrop acts like a prism and splits the white light into the seven colours which make up the **spectrum**.

Newton put forward the idea that, when white light falls on a prism, each colour is refracted at a different angle. The light is bent towards the base of the prism.

Procedure

Place the card with the narrow slit in front of the light source in the ray box.
Position the prism between the light source and the white screen.
Switch on the light source. Write what colours you see on the screen.

Ray of white light

Prism

White screen

r _ _ _

_____

_____

_____

_____

_____

v _ _ _ _ _ _

Answer these questions:

Which colour is refracted the most? _____

Which colour is refracted the least? _____

Which colour light travels the slowest? _____

Which colour light travels the quickest? _____

Add-on

Find out what the separation of colours is called.

How to create white light

What you need
- 3 projectors
- Red, green and blue filters
- White screen

Procedure

Put a different coloured filter into each projector. Set the projectors up so that the colours overlap as shown in the diagram below.

Name each of the colours.

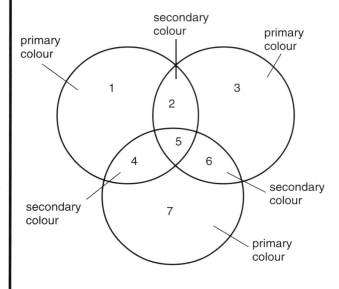

1 _____

2 _____

3 _____

4 _____

5 _____

6 _____

7 _____

White light can be created by using just three colours:

r __ __, g __ __ __ __ and blue. These are called the primary colours.

What do we call the colours that are formed when two primary colours are combined?

s __ __ __ __ __ __ __ __ __ colours.

Complete the following:

What colour is formed when red and green combine? _____

What colour is formed when green and blue combine? _____

Add-on

The colours on a TV screen are created using the three primary colours.
Can you think of another device which makes use of this same principle?

How to connect bulbs in series and in parallel

What you should know

A complete circuit must have no breaks in it.

For an electrical current to flow, electrons leave the negative terminal, and move through the wire to the positive terminal of the battery.

The symbol for a bulb is:

The symbol for a battery is:

The symbol for an electric wire is:

Procedure

Circuit diagram 1

Connecting bulbs in series

Connect the bulbs as shown in circuit diagram 1. Now place a third bulb in the circuit. What do you notice about the brightness of the bulbs?

_____

What happens if one of the bulbs is unscrewed from the bulb holder?

_____

Circuit diagram 2

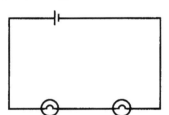

Connecting bulbs in parallel

Connect the bulbs as shown in circuit diagram 2. What happens if bulb B is unscrewed from the bulb holder?

_____

What is the advantage of wiring bulbs in parallel?

_____

Add-on

Are Christmas tree lights connected in series or in parallel?

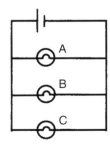

How to use a voltmeter and an ammeter

What you need
- 3 x 2.5v bulbs
- 3 bulb holders
- 2 x 1.5v batteries
- Connecting wire
- Ammeter
- Voltmeter

What you should know about voltmeters

A **voltmeter** has the symbol:

A voltmeter is used to measure the drop in voltage across a part of an electrical circuit. Always connect the voltmeter across the component(s) you want to investigate. The positive terminal of the voltmeter must be attached to the positive side of the component.

Procedure

Connect up the circuit as shown in the diagram.
Record the voltmeter reading across one bulb, two bulbs and then three bulbs.

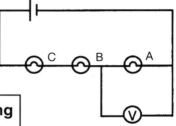

Voltmeter reading across 1 bulb (A)	Voltmeter reading across 2 bulbs (A & B)	Voltmeter reading across 3 bulbs (A, B & C)

What happens to the voltmeter readings? _____

_____

What you should know about ammeters

An **ammeter** is used to measure the electric current flowing through a circuit. An ammeter has the symbol:

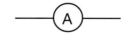

Current is measured in **amps** (A). The positive terminal of the ammeter must be connected to the positive terminal of the battery. Always connect an ammeter in series.

Procedure

Connect up the circuit as shown in the diagram. Record the ammeter readings with one bulb in the circuit, two bulbs and finally three bulbs.

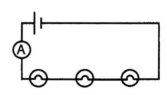

1 bulb	2 bulbs	3 bulbs
____ A	____ A	____ A

What happens to the current as the number of bulbs is increased?

_____

How to measure resistance

What you need
- 3 x 1.5v batteries
- 3 x 2.5v bulbs
- 3 bulb holders
- Switch
- Connecting wire
- Voltmeter
- Ammeter

Procedure

Connecting 3 bulbs in series

Connect the ammeter in series and the voltmeter in parallel as shown in circuit diagram 1.

Measure the current in amps, and the voltage drop across the three bulbs in series.

Circuit diagram 1

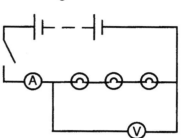

Calculate the resistance of the bulbs using the following formula:

$$R \text{ (resistance)} = \frac{\text{volts}}{\text{current}} \qquad R = \frac{}{} = \qquad \text{ohms}$$

Circuit diagram 2

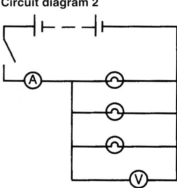

Connecting 3 bulbs in parallel

Connect the ammeter in series and the voltmeter in parallel as shown in circuit diagram 2.

Measure the current, and the voltage drop across the three bulbs in parallel.

Calculate the resistance of the bulbs using the following formula:

$$R \text{ (resistance)} = \frac{\text{volts}}{\text{current}} \qquad R = \frac{}{} = \qquad \text{ohms}$$

What is the difference in resistance measured when the bulbs are connected in series compared with when they are connected in parallel?

_____

_____

How to wire a plug

What you need
- Plug
- Flex
- Screwdriver
- Wire stripper

Safety
- Electricity is dangerous.
- Do not put your plug into an electric circuit.

What you should know

A fuse is the safety link in a circuit. If there is a fault in the circuit and too much current flows through the wire, the fuse will overheat and melt.
This will cause a break in the circuit.

Procedure

Trim back and remove the outer plastic casing from the flex.

Cut the three inner wires – the brown, blue and green/yellow to length.

Remove about 5 mm of the plastic covering from each of the three wires, to reveal the wire cores.

Lay the wires into the plug top. Do not kink the wires.

Connect the brown wire to the 'L' terminal.

Connect the blue wire to the 'N' terminal.

Connect the green/yellow wire to the 'E' terminal.

Secure the cable grip to the plastic casing.

Fit the cover to the plug.

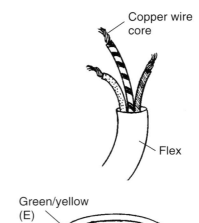

Copper wire core

Flex

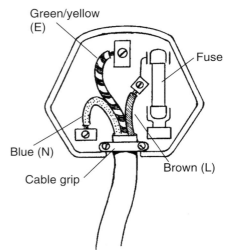

Green/yellow (E)

Fuse

Blue (N)

Cable grip

Brown (L)

What colour is the live wire? _____

What colour is the earth wire? _____

What colour is the neutral wire? _____

DO NOT PUT THE PLUG INTO A SOCKET

Learning about magnets

What you need
- 2 bar magnets
- String
- Copper
- Zinc
- Iron
- Brass
- Cobalt
- Nickel

What you should know

Suspend the bar magnet from a piece of string. Allow it to swing freely.

When it comes to rest, the end which points North is the north-seeking pole of the magnet. It is called N-pole for short.

What do we call the other end of the magnet?

String

Magnet

Procedure

Place the north pole of one magnet next to the south pole of another magnet.

N	S

What happens? _____

Place the south pole of one magnet next to the south pole of another magnet.

S	S

What happens? _____

Place each of the materials near the magnet. Put a tick ✔ in the table if the materials are attracted to the magnet.

Material	Magnetic?
Copper	
Zinc	
Iron	
Brass	
Cobalt	
Nickel	

Add-on

How can magnets lose their magnetism?
How can a piece of unmagnetized iron or steel be magnetized?

How to plot a magnetic field

What you need
- Bar magnet
- Plotting compass
- A4 white paper
- Pencil

What you should know
A **magnetic field** is the invisible force around a magnet.

Procedure

Place the bar magnet in the middle of a piece of A4 white paper.

Draw round the magnet to mark its position.

Place the plotting compass close to the end of the magnet.

Wait for the compass needle to settle.

Draw a cross on the paper next to the pointer.

Move the plotting compass on to the cross, so that the tail of the pointer is next to the cross.

Draw a second cross by the pointer.

Join up the crosses to form a pattern.

Repeat this procedure around the magnet. Start from a new position close to the magnet to repeat the plot, and 'map out' the whole magnetic field.

Where do you think the magnetic field is strongest?

_____

_____

Where do you think the field is weakest?

_____

_____

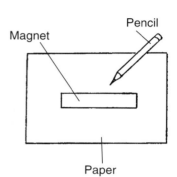

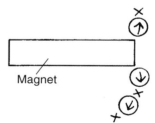

How to make an electromagnet

Safety
- Do not use more than 6v dc on a low voltage supply.
- With an electromagnet you can switch a magnet on and off.

Procedure

Take a length of insulated wire and wind 20 turns around a large iron nail. Connect the end of the wire to a low voltage supply.

Set the low voltage supply to 6v dc.

Place an ammeter in the circuit and keep the current constant. (Do not exceed 3 amps.)

Place a switch in the circuit. Switch on.

Put the end of the nail into a pile of paper clips. Count how many paper clips are attracted to the nail. Record the number in the table below.

Switch off the power supply.

Repeat using 30, 40, 50 and 60 turns. Keep the current constant. Record your results in the table.

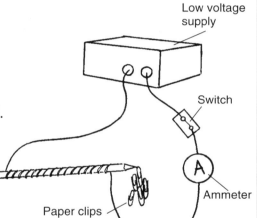

Number of turns	Number of paper clips
20	
30	
40	
50	
60	

What do the results tell you about the number of turns?

_____

Add-on
Where do you think you might find an electromagnet in a factory?

How to spot chemical and physical changes

Safety
- Handle chemicals with care.
- Wear safety goggles and tie long hair back.
- Place Bunsen burner in a safe position.

What you should know

Examples of **chemical changes** are: cooking a cake, a car rusting and coal burning. These changes cannot be reversed (changed back).

Examples of **physical changes** are: melting chocolate, adding salt to water and ice melting. These changes can be reversed.

Procedure

1. Place half a spatula of zinc oxide into a clean test tube.

2. Record the colour in the table before heating.

3. Light the Bunsen burner and position the air hole half open.

4. Heat the zinc oxide until the colour changes. Record what happens in the table.

5. Leave to cool in the test tube rack.

6. Record the colour after cooling.

7. Repeat steps 1 – 6 with copper carbonate and ammonium chloride.

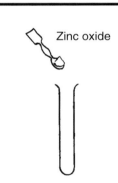

Zinc oxide

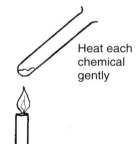

Heat each chemical gently

Name of chemical	Colour before heating	What happens when it is heated?	Colour after cooling	Physical or chemical change?

How to make a new compound from copper carbonate

Safety
- Always wear safety goggles.
- Tie long hair back.

Procedure

Zero the digital balance.

Weigh an empty crucible and record the mass: _____ g

Crucible + 3 g of copper carbonate

Weigh out exactly 3 g of copper carbonate into the crucible.

mass of crucible + copper carbonate = _____ g

Heat the contents gently. Stir the contents carefully. Use tongs to steady the crucible when you stir.

When the colour change is complete, turn off the Bunsen burner.
Leave the crucible to cool.

Spatula

Re-weigh the crucible when it is cool enough to handle.

mass of crucible + contents after heating = _____ g

Gentle heat

What do you think has caused the change in mass of the copper carbonate?

_____

What new substance has been formed? _____

What type of change is this? _____

Add-on
Finish the word equation for the reaction:

copper carbonate   +   heat ———→ _____   +   _____

How to investigate the effect of heat on copper (II) sulphate

What you need
- Evaporating basin
- Pipe clay triangle
- Tripod
- Bunsen burner
- Ceramic mat
- Spatula
- Copper (II) sulphate
- Digital balance
- Wash bottle
- Goggles

Safety
- Always wear safety goggles.
- Tie long hair back.
- Copper (II) sulphate is harmful.

Procedure

1. Zero the digital balance.

   Weigh an empty evaporating basin. Record the mass: _____ g

   Weigh out exactly 5 g of copper (II) sulphate into the evaporating basin.

   | mass of evaporating basin + copper (II) sulphate = _____ g |

   5g of 2 copper (II) sulphate

2. Heat the contents gently. The air hole on the Bunsen burner should be half open. Stir gently with a spatula.

   Then turn up the heat so that the air hole is fully open. Continue heating until the colour change is complete. Turn off the Bunsen burner and leave the evaporating basin to cool.

   Heat the contents gently

3. Re-weigh the evaporating basin when it is cool enough to handle.

   | mass of evaporating basin + copper (II) sulphate after heating = _____ g |

   What do you think has caused the change in mass of the copper (II) sulphate?

   _____

4. Add a few drops of water to the copper (II) sulphate. What happens?

   Add a few drops of water to the cool basin

   _____

   What type of change is this?

   _____

   Wash bottle

How to carry out food tests

Safety
- Iodine is harmful.
- Biuret solution is corrosive.
- Wear safety goggles.

Procedure

To test for starch

Drop a couple of drops of iodine solution on to a cut potato.

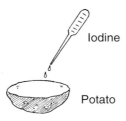

Iodine

Potato

The iodine will change from brown to blue/black if starch is present.

To test for glucose

Dissolve a spatula of glucose in a small amount of water in a test tube. Add about 10 drops of Benedict's solution. Heat the contents in a beaker of water.

Colour of solution before heating:

_____

Colour of solution after heating:

_____

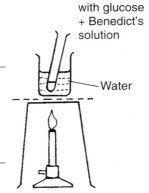

Test tube with glucose + Benedict's solution

Water

If the food contains glucose, the blue Benedict's solution will change to an orange/red colour.

To test for protein

Add about 10 drops of biuret solution to some egg white in a test tube.

Starting colour:

_____

Final colour:

_____

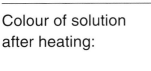

Test tube with biuret solution + egg white

The blue colour of the biuret solution will change to purple if protein is present.

To test for fat

Rub a small amount of fat on to a piece of filter paper, and hold it up to the light. Describe what you see.

_____

_____

Filter paper + fat

How much energy is stored in food?

Safety
- Wear safety goggles.

Procedure

Carefully place a peanut on the end of an optical pin.

Pour 15 cm³ of water into a boiling tube and record the temperature of the water.

Starting temperature of water: _____ °C

Place the boiling tube in the clamp stand.

Light the peanut using a Bunsen burner. Place it under the boiling tube.

When the peanut has finished burning, record the temperature of the water in the boiling tube.

Final temperature of water: _____ °C

Not all the heat energy from the peanut is transferred to the water.

Where else do you think the heat energy goes?

_____

_____

_____

Note: a crucible could be used instead of an optical pin in a cork.

Peanut

Optical pin

Cork

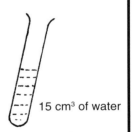

15 cm³ of water

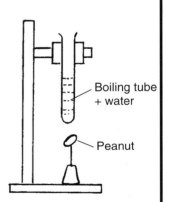

Boiling tube + water

Peanut

Add-on
Repeat the experiment using other foods.

How to test for the presence of starch in a leaf

What you need
- Geranium leaf (from plant that has been left in sunshine for several hours)
- 250 cm³ beaker
- Methylated spirits
- Iodine
- Boiling tube
- Forceps
- Glass rod
- White tile
- Kettle

Safety
- Always tie long hair back.
- Iodine is harmful.
- Methylated spirits are flammable.
- Take care when using boiling water.

Procedure

1. Place the leaf in a beaker of boiling water. This kills the leaf.

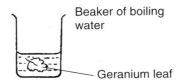

Remove the leaf using a pair of forceps.

2. Add methylated spirits to a boiling tube to a depth of 5 cm. Place the leaf in the boiling tube.

Refill the beaker with boiling water from a kettle. Place the boiling tube in the beaker. Leave for 10 minutes.

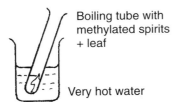

Why do you think the leaf is placed in the methylated spirits?

_____

_____

3. Remove the leaf using a glass rod and forceps. Place it in the hot water in the beaker.

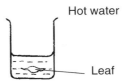

This will make the leaf softer.

4. Take the leaf out of the water and spread it out on the white tile. Place a few drops of iodine on to the leaf.

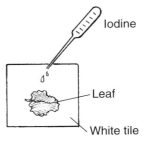

What colour does the leaf turn?

_____

Add-on
What food has the leaf produced?

How to test for a gas

What you need
- Splints
- Limewater
- Test tubes
- Manganese dioxide
- Hydrogen peroxide
- Marble chips
- Dilute hydrochloric acid
- Magnesium ribbon
- Delivery tube fitted with bung
- Goggles

Safety
- Wear safety goggles.
- Hydrogen peroxide should be handled with care as it can burn the skin.

Procedure

Testing for the presence of oxygen
Place a spatula of manganese dioxide in a test tube.

Add about 1 cm depth of hydrogen peroxide.

Hold a lighted splint to the mouth of the test tube.

If the split relights, the gas is oxygen.

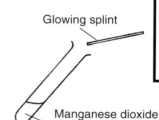

Glowing splint

Manganese dioxide in test tube

Testing for the presence of carbon dioxide
Place 3 marble chips in a test tube.

Add about 2 cm depth of dilute hydrochloric acid.

Bubble the gas being tested through limewater using the delivery tube. If the limewater turns milky, the gas is carbon dioxide.

Why do you think the limewater turns milky?

_____

What would carbon dioxide do to a glowing splint?

_____

What is carbon dioxide used for?

_____

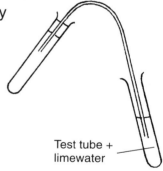

Test tube + limewater

Testing for the presence of hydrogen
Place a small piece of magnesium ribbon in a test tube. Add about 1 cm depth of dilute hydrochloric acid. Hold a lighted splint at the mouth of the test tube.

How do you know if hydrogen is produced?

_____

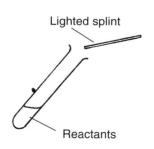

Lighted splint

Reactants

What causes pressure in gases?

What you need
- Bicycle pump
- 3 balloons
- Fridge
- Trough
- Boiling water

Safety
- Take care when using boiling water.

Procedure

Hold your finger over the outlet of a bicycle pump. Push the handle in. What do you feel with your finger?

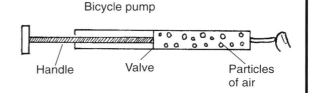

Bicycle pump

Handle   Valve   Particles of air

As the handle is pushed in, the particles of air are squashed into a smaller space.

Complete this statement:

When the volume of a gas decreases, its pressure _____

_____

Blow up three balloons so that they are all the same size.
- Place one balloon in the fridge
- Leave one balloon at room temperature
- Place the third balloon in a trough of boiling water.
  Compare the sizes of the balloons.

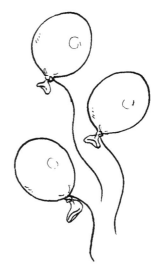

Answer these questions:

Which balloon appears to shrink in size?

_____

Which balloon appears to increase in size?

_____

Which balloon has the smallest inside pressure?

_____

Which balloon has the greatest inside pressure?

_____

What does this tell you about temperature and pressure?

_____

Diffusion in liquids and gases

What you need
- A litre beaker
- Length of capillary tubing
- Forceps
- Potassium permanganate (VII)
- Glass tube
- Clamp stand
- Cotton wool
- Hydrochloric acid
- Ammonia solution
- Goggles

Safety
- Your teacher will demonstrate these experiments.
- Always wear safety goggles.

Procedure

Diffusion in a liquid

Add cold water to a litre beaker until it is three quarters full. Allow the water to settle.

Using a pair of forceps, carefully drop a crystal of potassium permanganate (VII) down the glass tube to the bottom of the beaker.

Remove the glass tube from the beaker and leave the beaker for several hours.

What does this experiment prove?

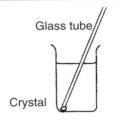

Glass tube

Crystal

Draw what you see.

_____

_____

Diffusion in a gas

Place a piece of cotton wool at each end of a glass tube. Attach the tube to a clamp stand.

Place a few drops of hydrochloric acid on the cotton wool at one end. Place a few drops of ammonia solution at the other end.

Wait several minutes. What happens?

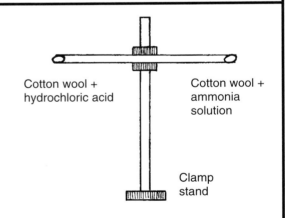

Cotton wool + hydrochloric acid

Cotton wool + ammonia solution

Clamp stand

_____

Why do you think the ammonium chloride forms near the hydrochloric acid end? What does this experiment prove?

_____

_____